THANK YOU GOD!

Kid's Nature Journal

This Nature Journal Belongs to:

_____

<u>_Prayer to Start a Day of Nature Exploration_</u>

Dear Heavenly Father,

I thank You this day for the incredible beauty of your creation, for all of the wonderful colors, smells, sounds, and all of the lovely living things You have made. Dear Father God, please open my heart and mind to learning the lessons which You want to show me in Your creation today.

I love You, Amen

Tips for the Young Explorer

In nature God has created many fascinating animals, plants, fungi, rocks, waterbodies, and landscapes for us to discover. Being observant is the first skill to exploring these wonders, and the following are some helpful hints for how you can be more observant:

1) Use your senses and record what you hear, smell, and see.
2) Look closer, there is always more going on in nature than it seems at first glance. Look close to see the tiny insects on a flower, the worms that are wiggling just beneath the soil's surface, the bugs living under a rock or in a log, and the fish, frogs, and insects swimming at the water's edge. What other things can you think to look closer at in nature?
3) Pay attention to the changes in nature from night to day, in different weather and temperature conditions, and during different seasons.
4) Be both still and active. Some animals are more secretive and will only come out if you are quiet and wait for them to reveal themselves. And other animals are less secretive and will show themselves as you actively explore.
5) Be kind and respectful to God's creatures. Do not poke or chase the animals, you would not like someone doing that to you, plus some animals while harmless if not provoked can bite or sting if they feel threatened.

Date:_____ Temperature:_____ Weather (Circle below):

What I saw: _____
_____
_____

What I heard: _____
_____
_____

What I smelled: _____
_____
_____

Today's Most Interesting Discovery

Morphology (What did it look like - Shape, Color, Size, etc...): _____
_____
_____
_____

Habitat (What was the place like where I found it): _____
_____
_____

Questions I have: _____
_____
_____
_____
_____

<u>My Nature Sketches</u>

Today I felt God showing me this in nature: _____

_____

_____

_____

_____

_____

_____

_____

Thank You God for all of Your Creations!

Learn to draw the organisms in God's creation by seeing if you can find and fill in all of the missing lines in the bottom picture so that it matches the top picture.

NATURE FACT: frogs do not need to drink water because they absorb it through their skin.

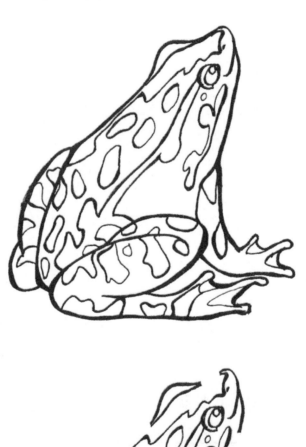

Date:_____ Temperature:_____ Weather (Circle below):

What I saw: _____
_____
_____

What I heard: _____
_____
_____

What I smelled: _____
_____
_____

Today's Most Interesting Discovery

Morphology (What did it look like - Shape, Color, Size, etc…): _____
_____
_____
_____

Habitat (What was the place like where I found it): _____
_____
_____

Questions I have: _____
_____
_____
_____
_____

My Nature Sketches

Today I felt God showing me this in nature: _____

_____

_____

_____

_____

_____

_____

_____

Thank You God for all of Your Creations!

Learn to draw the organisms in God's creation by seeing if you can find and fill in all of the missing lines in the bottom picture so that it matches the top picture.

NATURE FACT: The gulf fritillary butterfly is colored bright orange and black as a warning that it is poisonous so that possible predators will not eat it.

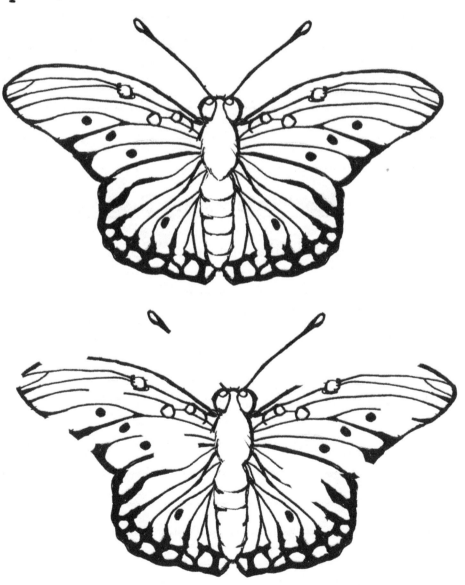

Date:_____ Temperature:_____ Weather (Circle below):

What I saw: _____
_____
_____

What I heard: _____
_____
_____

What I smelled: _____
_____
_____

Today's Most Interesting Discovery

Morphology (What did it look like - Shape, Color, Size, etc...): _____
_____
_____
_____
_____

Habitat (What was the place like where I found it): _____
_____
_____

Questions I have: _____
_____
_____
_____
_____

<u>My Nature Sketches</u>

Today I felt God showing me this in nature: _____

_____

_____

_____

_____

_____

_____

_____

Thank You God for all of Your Creations!

Learn to draw the organisms in God's creation by seeing if you can find and fill in all of the missing lines in the bottom picture so that it matches the top picture.

NATURE FACT: Strawberries are among the first fruits to ripen in the spring, and each of the little yellow, "seeds" on the outside of a strawberry are all individual fruits with a tiny seed inside each of them.

Date:_____ Temperature:_____ Weather (Circle below):

What I saw: _____
_____
_____

What I heard: _____
_____
_____

What I smelled: _____
_____
_____

Today's Most Interesting Discovery

Morphology (What did it look like - Shape, Color, Size, etc…): _____
_____
_____
_____

Habitat (What was the place like where I found it): _____
_____
_____

Questions I have: _____
_____
_____
_____
_____

<u>My Nature Sketches</u>

Today I felt God showing me this in nature: _____

_____

_____

_____

_____

_____

_____

_____

Thank You God for all of Your Creations!

Learn to draw the organisms in God's creation by seeing if you can find and fill in all of the missing lines in the bottom picture so that it matches the top picture.

NATURE FACT: The Eastern box turtle hibernates during the winter by burrowing deep under leaves and soil until the weather starts to warm up in April and May.

Date:_____ Temperature:_____ Weather (Circle below):

What I saw: _____

_____

_____

What I heard: _____

_____

_____

What I smelled: _____

_____

_____

Today's Most Interesting Discovery

Morphology (What did it look like - Shape, Color, Size, etc...): _____

_____

_____

_____

_____

Habitat (What was the place like where I found it): _____

_____

_____

Questions I have: _____

_____

_____

_____

_____

My Nature Sketches

Today I felt God showing me this in nature: _____

_____

_____

_____

_____

_____

_____

_____

Thank You God for all of Your Creations!

Learn to draw the organisms in God's creation by seeing if you can find and fill in all of the missing lines in the bottom picture so that it matches the top picture.

NATURE FACT: The parts of the lily pad you see floating on the water surface as the leaves and flowers are just a small part of the plant which has long and extensive stems and roots growing down into the pond's bottom.

Date:_____ Temperature:_____ Weather (Circle below):

What I saw: _____
_____
_____

What I heard: _____
_____
_____

What I smelled: _____
_____
_____

Today's Most Interesting Discovery

Morphology (What did it look like - Shape, Color, Size, etc...): _____
_____
_____
_____
_____

Habitat (What was the place like where I found it): _____
_____
_____

Questions I have: _____
_____
_____
_____
_____

My Nature Sketches

Today I felt God showing me this in nature: _____

_____

_____

_____

_____

_____

_____

_____

Thank You God for all of Your Creations!

Learn to draw the organisms in God's creation by seeing if you can find and fill in all of the missing lines in the bottom picture so that it matches the top picture.

NATURE FACT: Mice have amazing balance and can walk across narrow twigs and thin vines to get to a tasty treat.

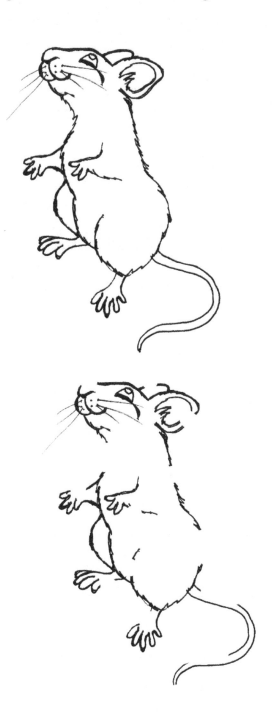

Date:_____ Temperature:_____ Weather (Circle below):

What I saw: _____

_____

_____

What I heard: _____

_____

_____

What I smelled: _____

_____

_____

Today's Most Interesting Discovery

Morphology (What did it look like - Shape, Color, Size, etc...): _____

_____

_____

_____

_____

Habitat (What was the place like where I found it): _____

_____

_____

Questions I have: _____

_____

_____

_____

_____

<u>My Nature Sketches</u>

Today I felt God showing me this in nature: _____

_____

_____

_____

_____

_____

_____

_____

Thank You God for all of Your Creations!

Learn to draw the organisms in God's creation by seeing if you can find and fill in all of the missing lines in the bottom picture so that it matches the top picture.

NATURE FACT: *Echinacea* flowers have large seeds at their centers which birds like goldfinches love to eat.

Date:_____ Temperature:_____ Weather (Circle below):

What I saw: _____
_____
_____

What I heard: _____
_____
_____

What I smelled: _____
_____
_____

Today's Most Interesting Discovery

Morphology (What did it look like - Shape, Color, Size, etc...): _____
_____
_____
_____

Habitat (What was the place like where I found it): _____
_____
_____

Questions I have: _____
_____
_____
_____
_____

My Nature Sketches

Today I felt God showing me this in nature: _____

_____

_____

_____

_____

_____

_____

_____

Thank You God for all of Your Creations!

Learn to draw the organisms in God's creation by seeing if you can find and fill in all of the missing lines in the bottom picture so that it matches the top picture.

NATURE FACT: Hummingbirds have big appetites because of their fast metabolism and feed on sugar water and flower nectar about every 10 to 15 minutes.

Date:_____ Temperature:_____ Weather (Circle below):

What I saw: _____
_____
_____

What I heard: _____
_____
_____

What I smelled: _____
_____
_____

Today's Most Interesting Discovery

Morphology (What did it look like - Shape, Color, Size, etc...): _____
_____
_____
_____

Habitat (What was the place like where I found it): _____
_____
_____

Questions I have: _____
_____
_____
_____
_____

My Nature Sketches

Today I felt God showing me this in nature: _____

_____

_____

_____

_____

_____

_____

_____

Thank You God for all of Your Creations!

Learn to draw the organisms in God's creation by seeing if you can find and fill in all of the missing lines in the bottom picture so that it matches the top picture.

NATURE FACT: Sunflower seeds are loved by many animals because they are a good source of fat, protein, and vitamins.

Date:_____ Temperature:_____ Weather (Circle below):

What I saw: _____
_____
_____

What I heard: _____
_____
_____

What I smelled: _____
_____
_____

Today's Most Interesting Discovery

Morphology (What did it look like - Shape, Color, Size, etc...): _____
_____
_____
_____

Habitat (What was the place like where I found it): _____
_____
_____

Questions I have: _____
_____
_____
_____
_____

My Nature Sketches

Today I felt God showing me this in nature: _____

_____

_____

_____

_____

_____

_____

Thank You God for all of Your Creations!

Learn to draw the organisms in God's creation by seeing if you can find and fill in all of the missing lines in the bottom picture so that it matches the top picture.

NATURE FACT: Monarch butterflies survive the cold winter months by migrating North America to Mexico where they enjoy the warm weather and sweet nectar of flowers through the Mexican winter.

Date: _____ Temperature: _____ Weather (Circle below):

What I saw: _____
_____
_____

What I heard: _____
_____
_____

What I smelled: _____
_____
_____

Today's Most Interesting Discovery

Morphology (What did it look like - Shape, Color, Size, etc...): _____
_____
_____
_____

Habitat (What was the place like where I found it): _____
_____
_____

Questions I have: _____
_____
_____
_____
_____

My Nature Sketches

Today I felt God showing me this in nature: _____
_____
_____
_____
_____
_____
_____
_____
_____

Thank You God for all of Your Creations!

Learn to draw the organisms in God's creation by seeing if you can find and fill in all of the missing lines in the bottom picture so that it matches the top picture.

NATURE FACT: Lanceleaf coreopsis is a favorite flower of many pollinator species like bees, butterflies, and birds.

Date:_____ Temperature:_____ Weather (Circle below):

What I saw: _____
_____
_____

What I heard: _____
_____
_____

What I smelled: _____
_____
_____

Today's Most Interesting Discovery

Morphology (What did it look like - Shape, Color, Size, etc...): _____
_____
_____
_____

Habitat (What was the place like where I found it): _____
_____
_____

Questions I have: _____
_____
_____
_____
_____

My Nature Sketches

Today I felt God showing me this in nature: _____

_____

_____

_____

_____

_____

_____

_____

Thank You God for all of Your Creations!

Learn to draw the organisms in God's creation by seeing if you can find and fill in all of the missing lines in the bottom picture so that it matches the top picture.

NATURE FACT: Not all ladybug beetles are red with black spots, some are orange or yellow with different markings.

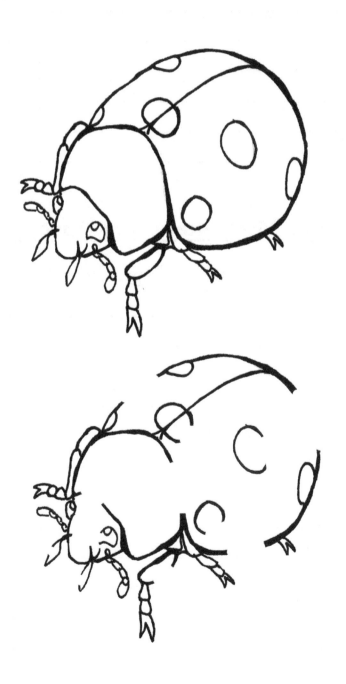

Date:_____ Temperature:_____ Weather (Circle below):

What I saw: _____
_____
_____

What I heard: _____
_____
_____

What I smelled: _____
_____
_____

Today's Most Interesting Discovery

Morphology (What did it look like - Shape, Color, Size, etc...): _____
_____
_____
_____

Habitat (What was the place like where I found it): _____
_____
_____

Questions I have: _____
_____
_____
_____
_____

My Nature Sketches

Today I felt God showing me this in nature: _____

_____

_____

_____

_____

_____

_____

_____

Thank You God for all of Your Creations!

Learn to draw the organisms in God's creation by seeing if you can find and fill in all of the missing lines in the bottom picture so that it matches the top picture.

NATURE FACT: Daffodils are one of the earliest flowers to bloom before most other plants in late winter or early spring, but deer and other animals do not consume them because they are poisonous and not safe to eat.

Date:_____ Temperature:_____ Weather (Circle below):

What I saw: _____
_____
_____

What I heard: _____
_____
_____

What I smelled: _____
_____
_____

Today's Most Interesting Discovery

Morphology (What did it look like - Shape, Color, Size, etc…): _____
_____
_____
_____

Habitat (What was the place like where I found it): _____
_____
_____

Questions I have: _____
_____
_____
_____
_____

My Nature Sketches

Today I felt God showing me this in nature: _____

_____

_____

_____

_____

_____

_____

_____

Thank You God for all of Your Creations!

Learn to draw the organisms in God's creation by seeing if you can find and fill in all of the missing lines in the bottom picture so that it matches the top picture.

NATURE FACT: Many rabbits change the color of their fur for winter, but the eastern cottontail keeps its brownish coat color all yearlong.

Date:_____ Temperature:_____ Weather (Circle below):

What I saw: _____
_____
_____

What I heard: _____
_____
_____

What I smelled: _____
_____
_____

Today's Most Interesting Discovery

Morphology (What did it look like - Shape, Color, Size, etc...): _____
_____
_____
_____
_____

Habitat (What was the place like where I found it): _____
_____
_____

Questions I have: _____
_____
_____
_____
_____

<u>My Nature Sketches</u>

Today I felt God showing me this in nature: _____

_____

_____

_____

_____

_____

_____

_____

Thank You God for all of Your Creations!

Learn to draw the organisms in God's creation by seeing if you can find and fill in all of the missing lines in the bottom picture so that it matches the top picture.

NATURE FACT: While most cherry tree varieties live an average of 30 years, the black cherry tree lives up to 250 years!

Date:_____ Temperature:_____ Weather (Circle below):

What I saw: _____
_____
_____

What I heard: _____
_____
_____

What I smelled: _____
_____
_____

Today's Most Interesting Discovery

Morphology (What did it look like - Shape, Color, Size, etc...): _____
_____
_____
_____

Habitat (What was the place like where I found it): _____
_____
_____

Questions I have: _____
_____
_____
_____
_____

My Nature Sketches

Today I felt God showing me this in nature: _____

_____

_____

_____

_____

_____

_____

_____

Thank You God for all of Your Creations!

Learn to draw the organisms in God's creation by seeing if you can find and fill in all of the missing lines in the bottom picture so that it matches the top picture.

NATURE FACT: Trout live in clean streams, rivers, and lakes, and they belong to the same family as salmon.

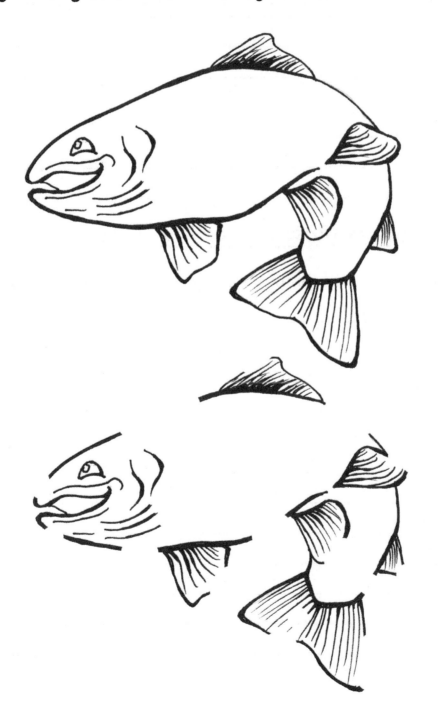

Date:_____ Temperature:_____ Weather (Circle below):

What I saw: _____
_____
_____

What I heard: _____
_____
_____

What I smelled: _____
_____
_____

Today's Most Interesting Discovery

Morphology (What did it look like - Shape, Color, Size, etc...): _____
_____
_____
_____

Habitat (What was the place like where I found it): _____
_____
_____

Questions I have: _____
_____
_____
_____
_____

My Nature Sketches

Today I felt God showing me this in nature: _____

_____

_____

_____

_____

_____

_____

_____

Thank You God for all of Your Creations!

Learn to draw the organisms in God's creation by seeing if you can find and fill in all of the missing lines in the bottom picture so that it matches the top picture.

NATURE FACT: Pollinators like bees prefer roses with less petals so that they can more easily get to the nectar and pollen at the center of the flower.

Date:_____ Temperature:_____ Weather (Circle below):

What I saw: _____
_____
_____

What I heard: _____
_____
_____

What I smelled: _____
_____
_____

Today's Most Interesting Discovery

Morphology (What did it look like - Shape, Color, Size, etc...): _____
_____
_____
_____

Habitat (What was the place like where I found it): _____
_____

Questions I have: _____
_____
_____
_____

My Nature Sketches

Today I felt God showing me this in nature: _____

_____

_____

_____

_____

_____

_____

_____

Thank You God for all of Your Creations!

Learn to draw the organisms in God's creation by seeing if you can find and fill in all of the missing lines in the bottom picture so that it matches the top picture.

NATURE FACT: Tiger beetles are hunters that use their well-designed long legs for running down and capturing their prey.

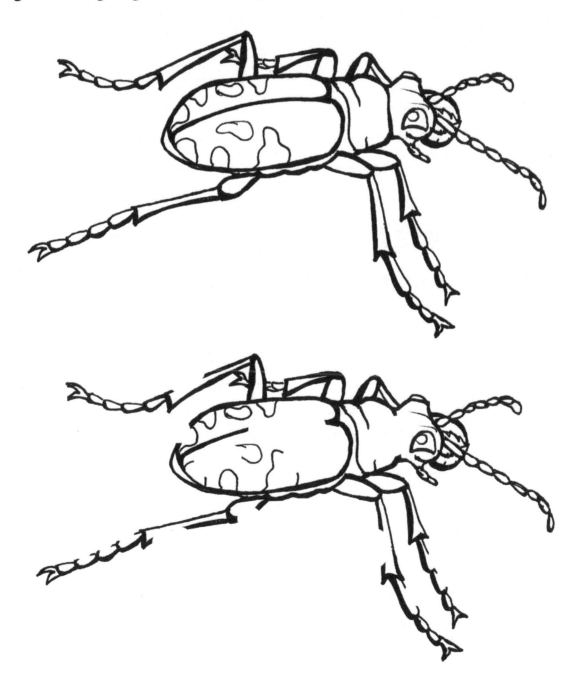

Date:_____ Temperature:_____ Weather (Circle below):

What I saw: _____
_____
_____

What I heard: _____
_____
_____

What I smelled: _____
_____
_____

Today's Most Interesting Discovery

Morphology (What did it look like - Shape, Color, Size, etc...): _____
_____
_____
_____

Habitat (What was the place like where I found it): _____
_____

Questions I have: _____
_____
_____
_____

My Nature Sketches

Today I felt God showing me this in nature: _____
_____
_____
_____
_____
_____
_____
_____

Thank You God for all of Your Creations!

Learn to draw the organisms in God's creation by seeing if you can find and fill in all of the missing lines in the bottom picture so that it matches the top picture.

NATURE FACT: *Dahlia* flowers were originally found in Mexico, and they come in almost every color, except for blue.

Date:_____ Temperature:_____ Weather (Circle below):

What I saw: _____
_____
_____

What I heard: _____
_____
_____

What I smelled: _____
_____
_____

Today's Most Interesting Discovery

Morphology (What did it look like - Shape, Color, Size, etc…): _____
_____
_____
_____

Habitat (What was the place like where I found it): _____
_____
_____

Questions I have: _____
_____
_____
_____
_____

My Nature Sketches

Today I felt God showing me this in nature: _____

_____

_____

_____

_____

_____

_____

_____

Thank You God for all of Your Creations!

Learn to draw the organisms in God's creation by seeing if you can find and fill in all of the missing lines in the bottom picture so that it matches the top picture.

NATURE FACT: Like many insects, tiger swallowtail butterfly females are larger than the males of their species.

Date:_____ Temperature:_____ Weather (Circle below):

What I saw: _____
_____
_____

What I heard: _____
_____
_____

What I smelled: _____
_____
_____

Today's Most Interesting Discovery

Morphology (What did it look like - Shape, Color, Size, etc...): _____
_____
_____
_____
_____

Habitat (What was the place like where I found it): _____
_____
_____

Questions I have: _____
_____
_____
_____
_____

My Nature Sketches

Today I felt God showing me this in nature: _____

_____

_____

_____

_____

_____

_____

_____

Thank You God for all of Your Creations!

Learn to draw the organisms in God's creation by seeing if you can find and fill in all of the missing lines in the bottom picture so that it matches the top picture.

NATURE FACT: Foxes' large ears are designed for excellent hearing which allows them to hear small sounds from far away. This is why they usually hear people coming and run away before anyone can see them.

Date:_____ Temperature:_____ Weather (Circle below):

What I saw: _____
_____
_____

What I heard: _____
_____
_____

What I smelled: _____
_____
_____

Today's Most Interesting Discovery

Morphology (What did it look like - Shape, Color, Size, etc...): _____
_____
_____
_____
_____

Habitat (What was the place like where I found it): _____
_____
_____

Questions I have: _____
_____
_____
_____
_____

My Nature Sketches

Today I felt God showing me this in nature: _____
_____
_____
_____
_____
_____
_____
_____

Thank You God for all of Your Creations!

Learn to draw the organisms in God's creation by seeing if you can find and fill in all of the missing lines in the bottom picture so that it matches the top picture.

NATURE FACT: Some mushrooms actually glow in the dark, this process is called bioluminescence.

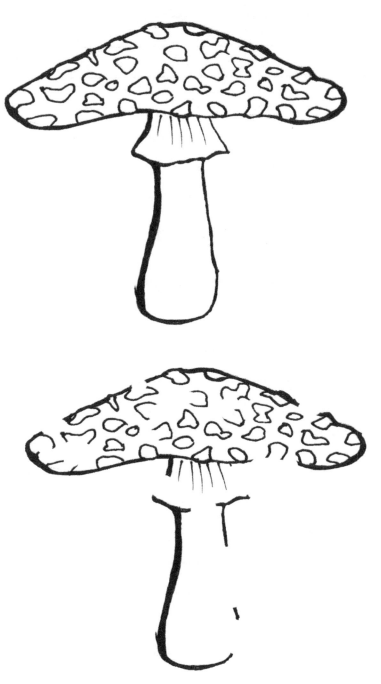

Date:_____ Temperature:_____ Weather (Circle below):

What I saw: _____
_____

What I heard: _____
_____

What I smelled: _____
_____
_____

Today's Most Interesting Discovery

Morphology (What did it look like - Shape, Color, Size, etc...): _____
_____
_____
_____

Habitat (What was the place like where I found it): _____
_____
_____

Questions I have: _____
_____
_____
_____
_____

My Nature Sketches

Today I felt God showing me this in nature: _____

_____

_____

_____

_____

_____

_____

_____

Thank You God for all of Your Creations!

Learn to draw the organisms in God's creation by seeing if you can find and fill in all of the missing lines in the bottom picture so that it matches the top picture.

NATURE FACT: Only female honey bees have a stinger and they use it to defend their hive if they feel threatened, so be kind and observe them without touching or bothering them.

Date:_____ Temperature:_____ Weather (Circle below):

What I saw: _____
_____
_____

What I heard: _____
_____
_____

What I smelled: _____
_____
_____

Today's Most Interesting Discovery

Morphology (What did it look like - Shape, Color, Size, etc...): _____
_____
_____
_____

Habitat (What was the place like where I found it): _____
_____
_____

Questions I have: _____
_____
_____
_____
_____

My Nature Sketches

Today I felt God showing me this in nature: _____

_____

_____

_____

_____

_____

_____

_____

Thank You God for all of Your Creations!

Learn to draw the organisms in God's creation by seeing if you can find and fill in all of the missing lines in the bottom picture so that it matches the top picture.

NATURE FACT: You may notice some similarities between daisies and sunflowers, and that is because the two flowers are related.

Date:_____ Temperature:_____ Weather (Circle below):

What I saw: _____
_____
_____

What I heard: _____
_____
_____

What I smelled: _____
_____
_____

Today's Most Interesting Discovery

Morphology (What did it look like - Shape, Color, Size, etc...): _____
_____
_____
_____

Habitat (What was the place like where I found it): _____
_____
_____

Questions I have: _____
_____
_____
_____
_____

My Nature Sketches

Today I felt God showing me this in nature: _____

_____

_____

_____

_____

_____

_____

_____

Thank You God for all of Your Creations!

Learn to draw the organisms in God's creation by seeing if you can find and fill in all of the missing lines in the bottom picture so that it matches the top picture.

NATURE FACT: Snails have eyes, but no ears, so they can see, but not hear.

Date:_____ Temperature:_____ Weather (Circle below):

What I saw: _____
_____
_____

What I heard: _____
_____
_____

What I smelled: _____
_____
_____

Today's Most Interesting Discovery

Morphology (What did it look like - Shape, Color, Size, etc...): _____
_____
_____
_____

Habitat (What was the place like where I found it): _____
_____
_____

Questions I have: _____
_____
_____
_____
_____

My Nature Sketches

Today I felt God showing me this in nature: _____

_____

_____

_____

_____

_____

_____

_____

Thank You God for all of Your Creations!

Learn to draw the organisms in God's creation by seeing if you can find and fill in all of the missing lines in the bottom picture so that it matches the top picture.

NATURE FACT: The blue jay raises or lowers the crest of feathers on top of its head based on its mood. When it is excited or aggressive the crest is raised, but when it is feeding or resting the crest is lowered.

Date:_____ Temperature:_____ Weather (Circle below):

What I saw: _____
_____
_____

What I heard: _____
_____
_____

What I smelled: _____
_____
_____

Today's Most Interesting Discovery

Morphology (What did it look like - Shape, Color, Size, etc…): _____
_____
_____
_____

Habitat (What was the place like where I found it): _____
_____
_____

Questions I have: _____
_____
_____
_____
_____

My Nature Sketches

Today I felt God showing me this in nature: _____

_____

_____

_____

_____

_____

_____

_____

Thank You God for all of Your Creations!

Learn to draw the organisms in God's creation by seeing if you can find and fill in all of the missing lines in the bottom picture so that it matches the top picture.

NATURE FACT: Even though most flowers have yellow or orange pollen, some varieties of poppy flowers have blue pollen, which you can see fuzzy bees covered with after feeding on those flowers.

Date:_____ Temperature:_____ Weather (Circle below):

What I saw: _____
_____
_____

What I heard: _____
_____
_____

What I smelled: _____
_____
_____

Today's Most Interesting Discovery

Morphology (What did it look like - Shape, Color, Size, etc...): _____
_____
_____
_____

Habitat (What was the place like where I found it): _____
_____
_____

Questions I have: _____
_____
_____
_____
_____

My Nature Sketches

Today I felt God showing me this in nature: _____

_____

_____

_____

_____

_____

_____

_____

Thank You God for all of Your Creations!

Learn to draw the organisms in God's creation by seeing if you can find and fill in all of the missing lines in the bottom picture so that it matches the top picture.

NATURE FACT: The goatweed leafwing butterfly has bright orange wings from the top, but underneath, they are a dull brown. So, when the butterflies fold their wings they look like dead leaves which camouflages them from predators and keeps them safe.

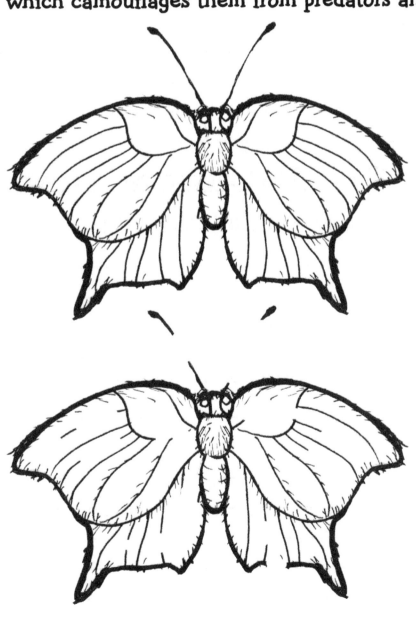

Date:_____ Temperature:_____ Weather (Circle below):

What I saw: _____
_____
_____

What I heard: _____
_____
_____

What I smelled: _____
_____
_____

Today's Most Interesting Discovery

Morphology (What did it look like - Shape, Color, Size, etc...): _____
_____
_____
_____

Habitat (What was the place like where I found it): _____
_____
_____

Questions I have: _____
_____
_____
_____
_____

My Nature Sketches

Today I felt God showing me this in nature: _____

_____

_____

_____

_____

_____

_____

_____

Thank You God for all of Your Creations!

Learn to draw the organisms in God's creation by seeing if you can find and fill in all of the missing lines in the bottom picture so that it matches the top picture.

NATURE FACT: Most insects have a pair of front and back wings for flight. Beetles however have strong shieldlike front wings not for flying, but for protecting their delicate back wings when not flying. To fly, they need to move their front wings and unfold their back wings.

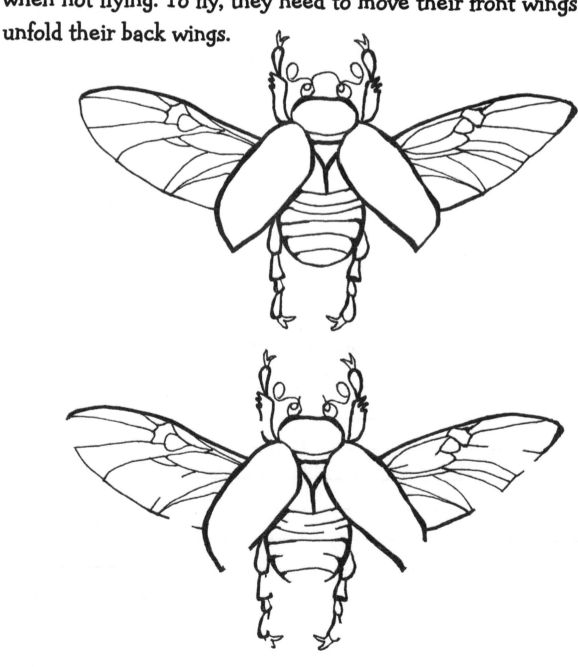

Date:_____ Temperature:_____ Weather (Circle below):

What I saw: _____
_____
_____

What I heard: _____
_____
_____

What I smelled: _____
_____
_____

Today's Most Interesting Discovery

Morphology (What did it look like - Shape, Color, Size, etc…): _____
_____
_____
_____

Habitat (What was the place like where I found it): _____
_____
_____

Questions I have: _____
_____
_____
_____
_____

My Nature Sketches

Today I felt God showing me this in nature: _____

_____

_____

_____

_____

_____

_____

_____

Thank You God for all of Your Creations!

Learn to draw the organisms in God's creation by seeing if you can find and fill in all of the missing lines in the bottom picture so that it matches the top picture.

NATURE FACT: Whitetail deer use their bright white tail to communicate with each other. For example, they wag and swish their tail to tell others everything is safe and okay, and they pick their tail straight up and flare their hairs when they are alarmed.

Date:_____ Temperature:_____ Weather (Circle below):

What I saw: _____
_____
_____

What I heard: _____
_____
_____

What I smelled: _____
_____
_____

Today's Most Interesting Discovery

Morphology (What did it look like - Shape, Color, Size, etc...): _____
_____
_____
_____
_____

Habitat (What was the place like where I found it): _____
_____
_____

Questions I have: _____
_____
_____
_____
_____

My Nature Sketches

Today I felt God showing me this in nature: _____

_____

_____

_____

_____

_____

_____

_____

Thank You God for all of Your Creations!

Learn to draw the organisms in God's creation by seeing if you can find and fill in all of the missing lines in the bottom picture so that it matches the top picture.

NATURE FACT: Wood duck families nest in tree holes or special boxes built for them. When the ducklings hatch, they jump from their nest high up in a tree into the water below.

Date:_____ Temperature:_____ Weather (Circle below):

What I saw: _____
_____
_____

What I heard: _____
_____
_____

What I smelled: _____
_____
_____

Today's Most Interesting Discovery

Morphology (What did it look like - Shape, Color, Size, etc...): _____
_____
_____
_____

Habitat (What was the place like where I found it): _____
_____
_____

Questions I have: _____
_____
_____
_____

My Nature Sketches

Today I felt God showing me this in nature: _____

_____

_____

_____

_____

_____

_____

_____

Thank You God for all of Your Creations!

Learn to draw the organisms in God's creation by seeing if you can find and fill in all of the missing lines in the bottom picture so that it matches the top picture.

NATURE FACT: Kingfisher birds have a sharp strong beak that they use like a sword to catch fish to eat.

Date:_____ Temperature:_____ Weather (Circle below):

What I saw: _____
_____
_____

What I heard: _____
_____
_____

What I smelled: _____
_____
_____

Today's Most Interesting Discovery

Morphology (What did it look like - Shape, Color, Size, etc...): _____
_____
_____
_____

Habitat (What was the place like where I found it): _____
_____
_____

Questions I have: _____
_____
_____
_____
_____

My Nature Sketches

Today I felt God showing me this in nature: _____

_____

_____

_____

_____

_____

_____

_____

Thank You God for all of Your Creations!

Learn to draw the organisms in God's creation by seeing if you can find and fill in all of the missing lines in the bottom picture so that it matches the top picture.

NATURE FACT: Water boatmen are very helpful for ponds and streams because they eat decaying matter and help keep the water clean.

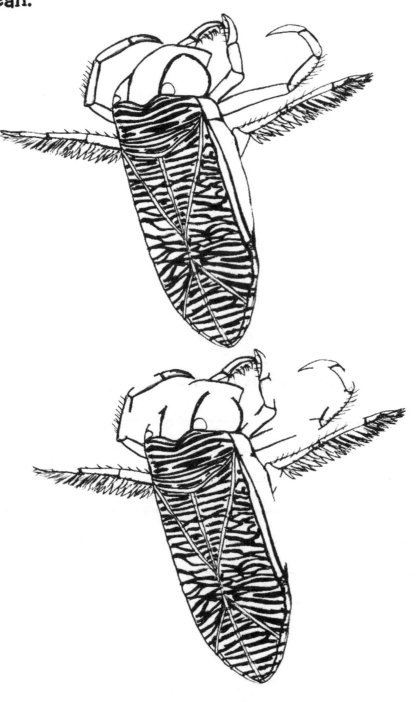

Date:_____ Temperature:_____ Weather (Circle below):

What I saw: _____
_____
_____

What I heard: _____
_____
_____

What I smelled: _____
_____
_____

Today's Most Interesting Discovery

Morphology (What did it look like - Shape, Color, Size, etc...): _____
_____
_____
_____

Habitat (What was the place like where I found it): _____
_____
_____

Questions I have: _____
_____
_____
_____
_____

My Nature Sketches

Today I felt God showing me this in nature: _____

_____

_____

_____

_____

_____

_____

_____

Thank You God for all of Your Creations!

Learn to draw the organisms in God's creation by seeing if you can find and fill in all of the missing lines in the bottom picture so that it matches the top picture.

NATURE FACT: Peony flowers are not just big and beautiful to look at, they have a sweet scent and sweeter nectar that attracts pollinators of all kinds, including ants.

Date:_____ Temperature:_____ Weather (Circle below):

What I saw: _____
_____
_____

What I heard: _____
_____
_____

What I smelled: _____
_____
_____

Today's Most Interesting Discovery

Morphology (What did it look like - Shape, Color, Size, etc…): _____
_____
_____
_____
_____

Habitat (What was the place like where I found it): _____
_____
_____

Questions I have: _____
_____
_____
_____
_____

My Nature Sketches

Today I felt God showing me this in nature: _____

_____

_____

_____

_____

_____

_____

_____

Thank You God for all of Your Creations!

Learn to draw the organisms in God's creation by seeing if you can find and fill in all of the missing lines in the bottom picture so that it matches the top picture.

NATURE FACT: The noise whitetail fawns make is called, "bleating" and the mother deer will come running if she hears her fawn bleat.

Date:_____ Temperature:_____ Weather (Circle below):

What I saw: _____
_____
_____

What I heard: _____
_____
_____

What I smelled: _____
_____
_____

Today's Most Interesting Discovery

Morphology (What did it look like - Shape, Color, Size, etc...): _____
_____
_____
_____

Habitat (What was the place like where I found it): _____
_____
_____

Questions I have: _____
_____
_____
_____
_____

My Nature Sketches

Today I felt God showing me this in nature: _____

_____

_____

_____

_____

_____

_____

_____

Thank You God for all of Your Creations!

Learn to draw the organisms in God's creation by seeing if you can find and fill in all of the missing lines in the bottom picture so that it matches the top picture.

NATURE FACT: The rainbow trout gets its name from its beautiful coloring including a red stripe on its sides, but the color of the back can be green, brown, or even blue depending on their habitat and their age.

Date:_____ Temperature:_____ Weather (Circle below):

What I saw: _____
_____
_____

What I heard: _____
_____
_____

What I smelled: _____
_____
_____

Today's Most Interesting Discovery

Morphology (What did it look like - Shape, Color, Size, etc...): _____
_____
_____
_____

Habitat (What was the place like where I found it): _____
_____
_____

Questions I have: _____
_____
_____
_____
_____

My Nature Sketches

Today I felt God showing me this in nature: _____

_____

_____

_____

_____

_____

_____

_____

Thank You God for all of Your Creations!

Learn to draw the organisms in God's creation by seeing if you can find and fill in all of the missing lines in the bottom picture so that it matches the top picture.

NATURE FACT: Squirrels live in nests made of moss, leaves, and sticks high up in the trees. If you look at the treetops in winter when the leaves have fallen you can more easily see these large leafy homes.

Date:_____ Temperature:_____ Weather (Circle below):

What I saw: _____
_____
_____

What I heard: _____
_____
_____

What I smelled: _____
_____
_____

Today's Most Interesting Discovery

Morphology (What did it look like - Shape, Color, Size, etc…): _____
_____
_____
_____

Habitat (What was the place like where I found it): _____
_____
_____

Questions I have: _____
_____
_____
_____
_____

<u>My Nature Sketches</u>

Today I felt God showing me this in nature: _____

_____

_____

_____

_____

_____

_____

_____

Thank You God for all of Your Creations!

Learn to draw the organisms in God's creation by seeing if you can find and fill in all of the missing lines in the bottom picture so that it matches the top picture.

NATURE FACT: Zinnia flowers come in many different shapes and sizes, but always with a yummy pollen and nectar filled center on which pollinating insects like to snack.

Date:_____ Temperature:_____ Weather (Circle below):

What I saw: _____
_____
_____

What I heard: _____
_____
_____

What I smelled: _____
_____
_____

Today's Most Interesting Discovery

Morphology (What did it look like - Shape, Color, Size, etc...): _____
_____
_____
_____
_____

Habitat (What was the place like where I found it): _____
_____
_____

Questions I have: _____
_____
_____
_____
_____

My Nature Sketches

Today I felt God showing me this in nature: _____

_____

_____

_____

_____

_____

_____

_____

Thank You God for all of Your Creations!

Learn to draw the organisms in God's creation by seeing if you can find and fill in all of the missing lines in the bottom picture so that it matches the top picture.

NATURE FACT: Mourning doves love to eat millet seeds, and when they take flight, their wings make a whistling sound.

Date:_____ Temperature:_____ Weather (Circle below):

What I saw: _____
_____
_____

What I heard: _____
_____
_____

What I smelled: _____
_____
_____

Today's Most Interesting Discovery

Morphology (What did it look like - Shape, Color, Size, etc...): _____
_____
_____
_____

Habitat (What was the place like where I found it): _____
_____
_____

Questions I have: _____
_____
_____
_____
_____

My Nature Sketches

Today I felt God showing me this in nature: _____

_____

_____

_____

_____

_____

_____

_____

Thank You God for all of Your Creations!

Learn to draw the organisms in God's creation by seeing if you can find and fill in all of the missing lines in the bottom picture so that it matches the top picture.

NATURE FACT: Bald eagles are amazing hunters and can reach speeds up to 200 miles an hour when they dive through the air to catch something to eat.

Dr. Diana Carle earned her PhD in Entomology, a Bachelor of Science in Biology and Anthropology as well as a minor in Classics. However, her most impactful educational experience was the nature-based homeschool program she attended from kindergarten through 6th grade. From exploring and sketching life along the pond's edge, to observing the miracle of butterfly metamorphosis, she learned at a young age that no classroom was as captivating as the one created by God in nature. She has spent over 13 years in environmental research and STEM education, creating and delivering a wide range of hands-on science-based curricula for undergraduate, graduate, and adult professional education courses at Rutgers University. Dr. Carle has served as a research associate on the Nurture thru Nature project, a grade 3-12 after school and summer nature-based program aimed at bolstering students' scholastic performance and social development. She ran New Jersey's mosquito control training and certification program where she educated health department personnel on responsible mosquito control which conserves both human and environmental health. She also founded Insect Diva, a nature inspired jewelry company which provides public outreach on conservation education. provides public outreach on conservation education. Dr. Carle currently creates nature-based educational materials, writes and illustrates children's books, and manages two conservation projects in: Monarch Butterfly Conservation and Pollinator Habitat Restoration.

www.DoctorDianaCarle.com

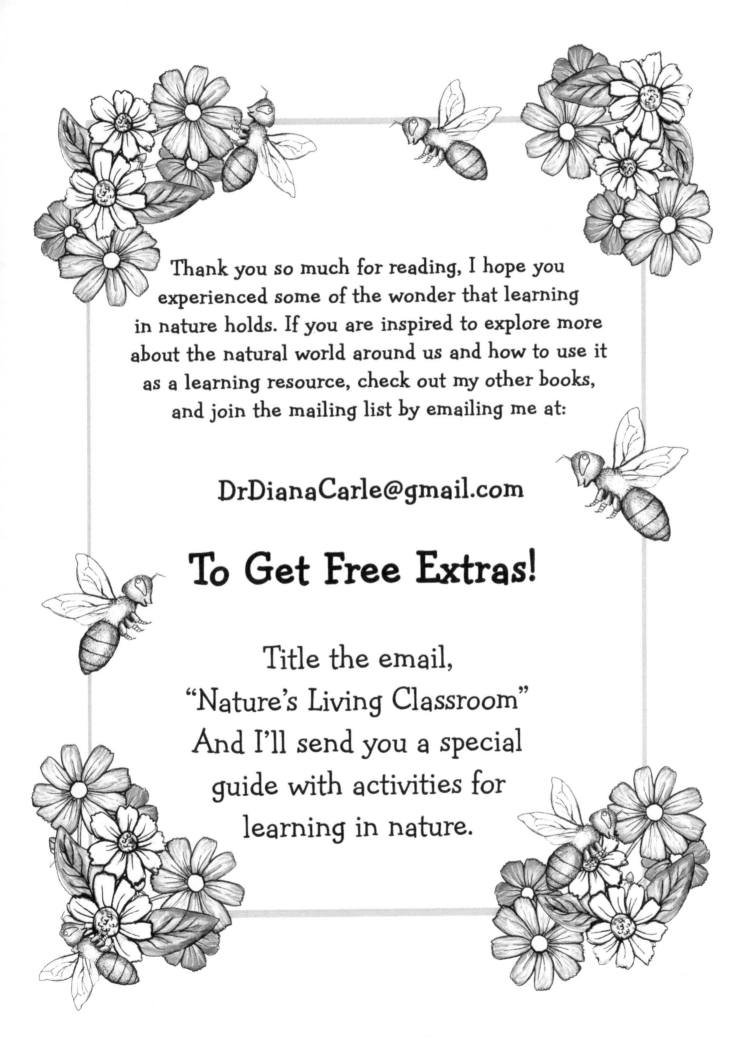

Thank you so much for reading, I hope you experienced some of the wonder that learning in nature holds. If you are inspired to explore more about the natural world around us and how to use it as a learning resource, check out my other books, and join the mailing list by emailing me at:

DrDianaCarle@gmail.com

To Get Free Extras!

Title the email,
"Nature's Living Classroom"
And I'll send you a special
guide with activities for
learning in nature.

Made in the USA
Monee, IL
01 December 2021

83574366R00070